Contents

This FLS Pupil Book is part of the Further Literacy Support programme produced by the Primary National Strategy (Department for Education and Skills).

Distributed by Heinemann, Ginn and Rigby
Divisions of Harcourt Education Ltd, Halley Court, Jordan Hill, Oxford OX2 8EJ

ISBN: 0435 035010

Also available from Heinemann, Ginn and Rigby FLS Homework Sheets (ISBN 0435 035029)
For orders or more information call 01865 888001 or go to www.myprimary.co.uk/fls

08 07 06 05 04
10 9 8 7 6 5 4 3 2

Printed in the UK by Ashford Colour Press, Gosport, Hants.

Acknowledgement
Extract from *Dr Xargle's Book of Earthlets* by Jeanne Willis and illustrated by Tony Ross © Jeanne Willis and Tony Ross 1988. Reproduced by kind permission of the publisher, Andersen Press.

Introduction

This is your FLS Book. It includes ideas, reminders, planning guides and record sheets that will help you with your writing. Sometimes you will use the book with a partner and sometimes you will use it on your own. You will be able to use this book in several different ways:

- it will remind you of things you need to learn;
- it will jog your memory about important points;
- it will help you to try out different writing techniques;
- it will help you to plan your work;
- it will give you ideas on how to improve what you have written;
- it will help you to see the progress you have made.

It will help you to learn more easily, but it will also set some challenges. As you work through this book, it will build into a record of your success as you meet those challenges and show just how well you can do.

All the ideas in this book are really practical and helpful – you'll be able to start using them in your writing straight away. So it won't be long before you'll see just how much you're learning in FLS and how much your work is improving.

This book is going to be something you'll be really proud of. Take care of it and use it to show yourself – and anybody else – just how well you can learn.

VIP Better meals for life!

Target plan

Week 1
Evaluating adverts and identifying key features to use when designing an advert

Week 2
Writing a persuasive leaflet

Week 3
Arguing a point of view

Week 4
Completing and improving the argument: rewriting as a letter written to persuade

I am learning to choose words carefully so that I can persuade people with my writing.

I am learning to make notes to plan my writing and turn them into sentences.

I am learning to organise my writing to present information clearly.

I am learning to edit and improve my writing, checking that I have written a good, persuasive argument.

When I am writing to persuade I can:

- choose how to present my ideas if I want to persuade somebody, e.g. an advert, a leaflet, a letter;
- use note making as a way of collecting and organising my ideas before I write;
- choose words carefully, adding adjectives, adverbs and powerful verbs to help get my message across;
- compose sentences carefully, choosing whether to use long or short sentences to make a particular point;
- use paragraphs to organise my ideas in a longer piece of writing;
- check and correct my own spellings;
- edit and re-draft my own writing;
- reflect on my own writing, using a checklist to help me decide whether I have got better at persuasive writing.

LET ME PERSUADE YOU

Checklist of key features of effective adverts

Techniques that advertisers use to grab your attention include:

- **snappy slogans**

  e.g. 'Mustard Munch
   – the snack that kicks back'

- **exaggeration**

  e.g. 'the holiday of a lifetime'

- **intriguing questions**

  e.g. 'How would you feel if you never needed to tidy your room again?'

- **appealing adjectives**

  e.g. 'velvety chocolate'

- **wordplay**

  e.g. 'Use Tubb's Margarine – it's a spreading habit.'

- **tempting descriptions of benefits**

  e.g. 'After just ten minutes in a Mello bubble bath, you'll feel soothed, relaxed and refreshed.'

Intriguing question – to catch reader's attention

Catchy rhyme

[pro]mpting [de]scription [of the] [be]nefits [of the] [pro]duct

[Wo]rdplay

[Sn]appy [slo]gan

Who is your clothes' best friend – and dirt's worst enemy?

SUDZ! It doubles the bubbles.

Exaggeration

Gentle SUDZ with mighty foam is guaranteed to leave your dirtiest washing super clean and fragrant fresh.

It's the washing powder that beats the rest into the dirt.

Appealing adjectives to create an impression

SUDZ – washing powder with attitude!

Before washing with SUDZ   After washing with SUDZ

SUDZ

Analysing adverts

Choose one of the adverts you looked at in guided reading and then analyse it using the grid below. (*One example has been done for you.*)

Feature	Advert 1 'SUDZ'	Advert 2
slogans	'Washing powder with attitude'	
exaggeration	It says that it beats all the other powders. This is probably an exaggeration.	
questions	'Who is your clothes' best friend – and dirt's worst enemy?'	
adjectives	Yes, it uses a lot of adjectives, like 'mighty', 'super' and 'fragrant'.	
wordplay	Yes, there is a rhyme: 'It doubles the bubbles.'	
benefits	It says that even the dirtiest washing will come out clean.	

Best advert scorecard			
	VIP advert 1	VIP advert 2	VIP advert 3
slogans			
exaggeration			
questions			
adjectives			
word play			
benefits			
total			

VIP advert template

Using adjectives to create slogans

Think of adjectives that could be used in an advert to sell the products in the table below. You may want to use a thesaurus to help you. For each product, try to find at least three adjectives which make the product sound really interesting or attractive.

The first one has been done for you.

Product (noun)	Adjectives
mints	*juicy* *smooth* *munchy*
cola	
toothpaste	
book	
trainers	

Think of some more products, and choose suitable adjectives to make them sound attractive.

Product (noun)	Adjectives

Key features of leaflets

Leaflets:

- describe a product and its benefits;
- are written in sentences.

Checklist of persuasive techniques

Tips for making your writing more persuasive:

- choose powerful verbs to use;

- select the adjectives and adverbs carefully;

- use exaggeration;

- use **bold** and CAPITAL letters to add emphasis.

Planning your leaflet

Discuss your **VIP** product with a partner, describing the product and its benefits clearly.

Use the questions below to help you to plan the ideas for your leaflet. Remember that this is a plan, so you only need to make brief notes.

Name and slogan of product	
(Get these from your advert!)	
Description of product	
What is it?	
Buyer of product	
Who is it for?	
Availability of product	
Where can you get it?	
Benefits of product	
What does it do for you?	
Why should you buy it?	

Making your leaflet more persuasive

In yesterday's supported session, you were looking at **persuasive** techniques. Today you are going to use some of these techniques to improve your leaflet.

- Swap leaflets with your partner and ask them to identify:

- one adjective
- one adverb
- one verb

that could be improved to make the leaflet more persuasive.

- Now make changes to any words that your partner has suggested!

- Can you find any other adjectives, adverbs or verbs that you could improve to make your leaflet more persuasive?

What a rip off!

Although not everyone would agree, I believe that professional footballers earn far too much money and I think that their exorbitant wages should be cut immediately. I have several reasons to support my point of view.

Firstly, some footballers in the Premier League earn more in one week than hardworking nurses and firemen earn in a whole year. Nurses and firemen are people who constantly save lives and on top of this, firemen bravely risk their own lives. What do footballers do? Kick a ball around a field for 90 minutes. This is clearly not fair!

In addition, footballers do not spend as much time at work (if you can call it that!) as most people. Although they train daily, this is normally for not more than three hours, while most people work at least seven hours daily. Furthermore, they have three months' holiday a year when the season ends, whereas most people have only four weeks' holiday a year.

In conclusion, it is clear that, compared to others, footballers earn far too much money. Their wages should be reduced and more money given to people who deserve it more!

Effective arguments:

- try to get the reader on your side;

- back up your arguments with evidence;

- use persuasive language.

'And my point is ...'

Use the checklist of persuasive techniques to identify the techniques the author has used to persuade the reader in the letter below. Annotate the sheet if you want to!

We should ban playtime at school

In my opinion children at primary school do not need a playtime.

The most important reason for this is that playtimes waste work time. The children need to spend more time on their English or Maths work. No one could argue with the importance of these subjects, and the more time spent by children practising them, the better.

In addition to this, playtimes are too dangerous. Little children get knocked over by bigger children and get hit by balls. Most injuries to children at school happen during playtime.

Finally, playtimes are bad for teachers. Many teachers are too old to run around and so they get too cold outside.

Therefore, I believe it would be best if playtimes were banned.

Argument planning framework

Use this framework to organise the ideas for your letter.

There are some useful connectives at the bottom of each box that will help you when drafting your argument.

Opening paragraph
Why you are writing and what you want to happen...

Although not everyone would agree...
I believe that...

Main reason to support your argument
... add evidence to back up your point of view...

Firstly...
The most important point is...

Further reason to support your argument
... add evidence to back up your point of view...

Furthermore...
In addition...

Concluding paragraph
Summarise the main points...
Restate your point of view and what you want to happen...

In conclusion...
Therefore...

Writing an argument template:

Please do not cancel children's TV

Letter writing template:

Please do not cancel children's TV

Dear

Yours faithfully

Checklist of improving arguments

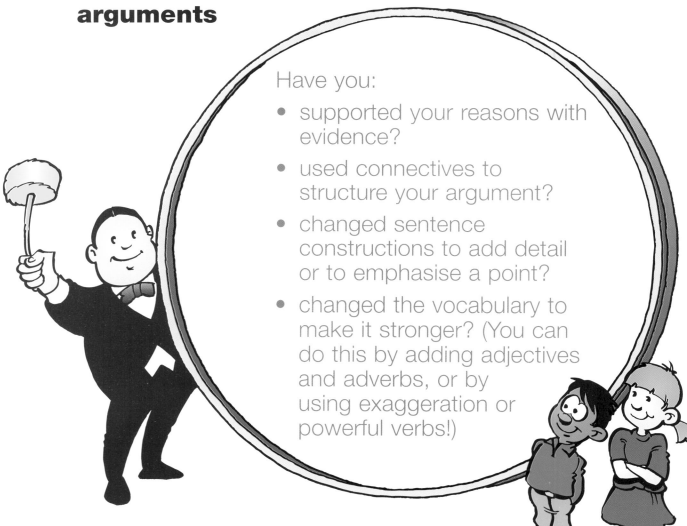

Have you:

- supported your reasons with evidence?

- used connectives to structure your argument?

- changed sentence constructions to add detail or to emphasise a point?

- changed the vocabulary to make it stronger? (You can do this by adding adjectives and adverbs, or by using exaggeration or powerful verbs!)

Connect your ideas

Fill in the blanks by selecting connectives from around the edge to structure the argument.

Soap operas are silly!

Many people will disagree, but I think soap operas are truly silly.

rthermore

Besides

_____ , the characters are unrealistic. They are always arguing and fighting with each other.
_____ , they do not ever seem to go to work.
_____ , the actors playing the characters are continually changing. Do they think we don't notice this?

so

In addition

_____ , the storylines are boring. Who is really interested in whether a launderette closes down?
_____ this, the plots are also unrealistic. When was the last time someone you knew drowned and then came back to life five years later?

conclusion

Firstly

_____ , some people say that soap operas are interesting because they are just like real life.
_____ , if this is so, why don't we see the characters going to the supermarket or school?

_____ , I think soap operas are silly and should be replaced with more documentaries.

On the other hand

However

Editing prompt sheet

In your supported and guided sessions, you have started to improve your writing by reviewing the content and language that you used in your argument. This is called **re-drafting**. Now you are going to continue this process by reviewing the punctuation and spelling. This is called **editing**.

This checklist is a list of things that you need to think about when editing. Use it to help you! When you have finished, swap arguments with a partner and check each other's writing.

Editing your writing

Spelling

☐ Check that you have spelt any high-frequency words correctly – use your spelling strategies to help you.

☐ Underline five words that you had difficulty spelling. Try to spell them using one of the spelling strategies you have learned and then check them using a dictionary.

Punctuation

☐ Read through your writing and check that you have not missed any words out.

☐ Have you used capital letters at the beginning of each sentence and put a full stop at the end?

☐ Does each of your sentences make sense on its own?

☐ Have you used question marks when you have written a question?

☐ Have you used exclamation marks to show when you have said something that is surprising?

☐ Do you need to use a comma to separate the different clauses (ideas) within a sentence?

Persuasive writing checklist

When writing a persuasive text I can:

- [ ] open by stating the point of view I will be arguing;
- [ ] give a range of points to support my point of view;
- [ ] provide evidence and information to back up my points;
- [ ] sequence my points in order of importance;
- [ ] address counter-arguments;
- [ ] get the reader on my side as quickly as possible but still appear reasonable;
- [ ] persuade the reader that everyone else agrees with my point of view by using phrases such as: 'we all know that ... '; 'everyone agrees that ... ';
- [ ] write short sentences to emphasise key points;
- [ ] use a question or exclamation to draw the reader in;
- [ ] use powerful verbs, adjectives and adverbs to make an impact;
- [ ] use exaggeration;
- [ ] use strong language to provoke a reaction;
- [ ] use slogans and other plays on words to draw the reader in;
- [ ] use connectives to link the ideas in each paragraph, e.g. 'however', 'although', 'because';
- [ ] conclude by summarising and restating my opening position;
- [ ] write in the present tense.

My target bank

Week 1 Target

I am learning to choose words carefully so that I can persuade people with my writing.

Week 2 Target

I am learning to make notes to plan my writing and turn them into sentences.

Week 3 Target

I am learning to organise my writing to present information clearly.

Week 4 Target

I am learning to edit and re-draft my writing, checking that I have written a good persuasive argument.

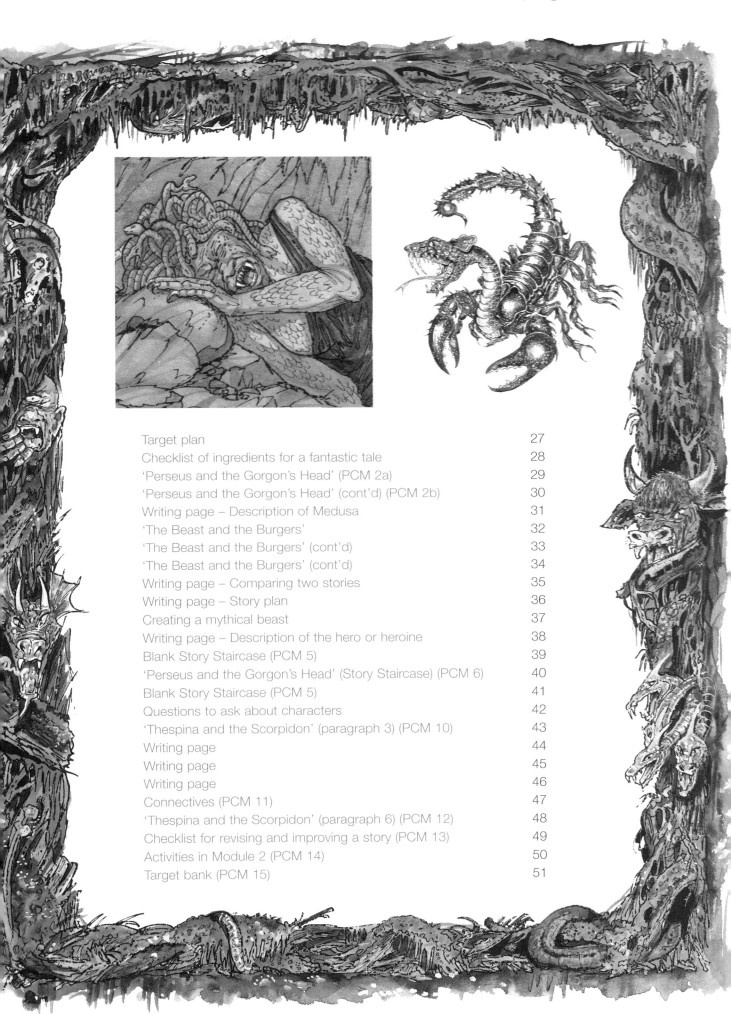

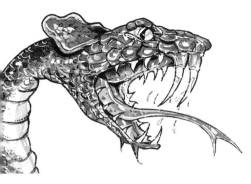

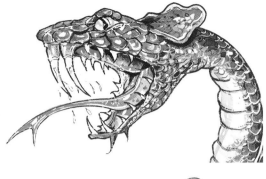

Target plan

Week 5	Week 6	Week 7	Week 8
Evaluating myths and identifying key features to use as a model for writing	Planning story plots	Developing a story from a plan	Completing and reviewing a story

I am learning to identify features in stories and use these to plan my own writing.	I am learning to use paragraphs to organise a story plot and move the action on.	I am learning to write a story that engages my readers and builds up to the most exciting part.	I am learning to resolve the problem in my story with a satisfying ending, and improve it to make it more interesting to a reader.

When I am writing a story I can:

- use story structures from stories I've read;
- plan a whole story with a clear sequence of events;
- write a good opening to introduce the setting and characters and give a clue about the plot;
- build up events to the most exciting part and resolve the problems at the end;
- write a satisfying ending;
- arrange the story into paragraphs to move the action on;
- describe good and bad characters effectively;
- use some short sentences for effect, and combine others into complex sentences;
- review, edit and correct my writing to produce a final draft;
- plan and write my story with a real reader in mind.

Checklist of ingredients for a fantastic tale

Ingredients for a fantastic tale	Notes
An interesting setting	
• When does it take place?	
• Where does it take place?	
• Does it provide details that catch your interest and set the mood of the story?	
A fantastical beast	
• What does it look like?	
• How does it behave?	
• Is it described in detail?	
A detailed description of the struggle to solve the problem	
• How does the hero/heroine find the beast? • Is there a journey involved?	
• What does the beast do? • Is there a conflict?	
• Does the hero/heroine have any help in solving the problem, e.g. special powers, friends?	
A good ending	
• How is the problem resolved? • Who wins the struggle?	
• Does the hero/heroine receive a reward?	

A Greek Myth
Perseus and the Gorgon's Head

Long ago, Polydectes was king of Seriphos, in a land called Greece. A mother and son, called Danae and Perseus, lived in the palace. The king wanted to marry Danae but she kept refusing him. Eventually he sent his guards to get her.

Perseus was strong and feared nothing. He fought the guards and defended his mother. The king wanted to get rid of Perseus, so he sent him on a dangerous mission. Perseus had to go and fetch the head of the Gorgon, Medusa.

Medusa was one of three monstrous sisters. They could turn men to stone just by looking at them.

Perseus had a long and difficult journey to find the Gorgons. The gods gave him two things to help him: a shiny shield and a sickle to cut off Medusa's head. He tricked the Three Grey Sisters into telling him where to find Medusa. They sent him to the Ocean Nymphs. The Nymphs hated Medusa and agreed to help. They gave him winged sandals so that he could fly to the right place, and a helmet to make him invisible.

Perseus reached the land where the Gorgons lived. He heard their terrible snoring, and the snakes on their heads hissing loudly. He looked in the shield to see their reflection. Then he cut off Medusa's head. The other Gorgons woke up, but Perseus put on the helmet and flew away.

It was a long and difficult journey. Eventually Perseus got back to Seriphos. He went to King Polydectes and showed him the Gorgon's head. The King was turned to stone. Perseus and his mother were safe at last.

A description of Medusa

The Beast and the Burgers

(An alternative text for Independent session, Week 5)

Last year, in a small town not far from here, the most terrible beast that had ever been seen roamed the streets every night. During the day it seemed like any other normal town. Everyone was happy, and at lunchtime they went to one place for their lunch – Best's Burgers – because they really did serve the most delicious burgers you have ever tasted.

Everything changed when night fell. The people rushed home, locked their doors and hid in fright as the beast came up out of the sewers and prowled the streets looking for food. Everybody said it would eat anything – rubbish from the dustbins, old tin cans, footballs and bikes, and even children (although no one could actually remember this happening). The beast was as long as a bus and had a body like a crocodile. It lived deep in the sewers and was covered in smelly, dirty slime. No one dared to stop it because it could breathe fire.

Jez Best lived with her Dad in the flat above Best's Burgers. But even with eating her Dad's burgers, Jez was small and skinny. She was incredibly shy and often got picked on at school by the bigger children. However, the children at school did not know the real Jez. She may have been small but she was very brave and she always knew how to sort out her Dad's problems.

Best's Burgers was facing the biggest problem ever. The beast had found out that Best's burgers really were the best and night after night it came back for more and more burgers. Dad was getting more and more worried because soon he would have no burgers left to sell. No one seemed to know what to do… except Jez. She knew she had to find a way to get rid of the beast so that Dad could keep making the best burgers in town.

That night she crept downstairs and waited in the burger bar. Pretty soon the beast came lumbering towards the door and burnt it down with one fiery breath. Jez, hiding behind the counter, caught a glimpse of its huge crocodile-like body, dripping with disgusting slime. The beast set to, wolfing down the juicy burgers that Jez had left out for it. (Well, she wanted to be sure that she would not be eaten!) The beast was huge, but its eyes looked sad and even a bit frightened. Every now and again it would stop eating and groan loudly. Jez could hardly believe her eyes – the beast seemed to have a stomach ache!

Eventually, the beast gave one more miserable groan and made its way back out of the burger bar. Jez followed at a safe distance, looking out for the trail of slime. The beast came to an open drain cover and squeezed its way in. As its tail disappeared, Jez took a deep breath of fresh air and climbed down into the sewers after it. It was so slimy, dark and smelly that it was hard to find the way, but luckily Jez had remembered to bring her torch. The beast reached a small tunnel and made its way in, and then there were a lot more groans and moans until finally the sounds stopped.

The beast was asleep… or so she thought. Jez turned to make her way back out of the sewer when her torch slipped out of her hand and fell crashing to the floor. She heard terrible groans and moans and then, to her amazement… a deep rasping voice. 'Who are you? What are you doing here?' At first, Jez was frozen with fear. Her instinct was to run, but then she remembered the beast's fiery breath – she could never run away from that. There was nothing for it but to explain about Dad, Best's Burgers and the town. 'Why can't you just go away and leave us all in peace?' she finished with a wail.

The beast replied mournfully, 'Do you think I want to be stuck down here? I was just an ordinary pet until somebody flushed me down the toilet. I ended up down here, growing bigger and bigger, with nothing good to eat and nowhere to swim.' The beast went on to explain how all those old bikes and dustbins gave him terrible indigestion and made him groan in agony. 'I would leave the town alone if only I had somewhere else to go.'

Jez left as quickly as she could, slithering and sliding her way back out of the sewer. All the while she was using her usual skill of working out problems and she was beginning to think up a plan.

The next morning, Jez explained it all to her Dad. At first, he had trouble getting used to the idea that she had actually followed the beast, but eventually she was sure that he was listening.
'Dad, we need to get it out of the sewers. It hasn't got enough room or any water to swim in. And all those old bikes and dustbins must be giving it indigestion. No wonder it groans all the time.'

'But Jez, what can we possibly do?' sighed Dad.
'We'll lure it into your lorry with a trail of burgers. Then we can take it all the way to
Scotland. We'll find a deep lake miles from anywhere and set it free. I'm sure that it will be
happier eating fish.'
'Jez, you're amazing!' exclaimed Dad, looking at her proudly. 'We'll do it tonight.'

And that's exactly what they did. The hardest part was getting the beast into the lorry. The
front fitted in all right but the beast's tail was hanging out of the back. Luckily, it was still dark
as they drove up to Scotland, eventually reaching a remote lake surrounded by mountains.
Jez and her Dad cowered behind the doors as the beast emerged and looked around.
Instead of breathing fire, it just made a happy, gurgling sound, and they could have sworn
they saw it wagging its tail. The beast made its way down to the lake side and plunged in. It
disappeared into the cold, dark water and pretty soon there was nothing to be seen, not
even a ripple.

Jez and her Dad hugged each other and began the long drive home. They were exhausted,
but that evening they re-opened Best's Burgers. Within days, the queues were stretching
down the street, not only at lunchtime, but every
evening as well. Best's Burgers were doing better
than ever.

No one else ever knew what had happened to the
beast. Jez was too shy to talk about it and Dad
was too busy with the burgers. But somehow
people seemed to notice a change in Jez. Although
she was still quiet and shy, the big children didn't
pick on her any more. Memories of the beast faded
quickly and now it is just a fantastic tale that
parents tell their children. However, there is a lake in
Scotland where, it is said, you can sometimes see
an enormous beast appearing from the water at
night, making a strangely happy gurgling sound.

Comparing two stories

Story plan

Creating a mythical beast

Head	Body	What it does

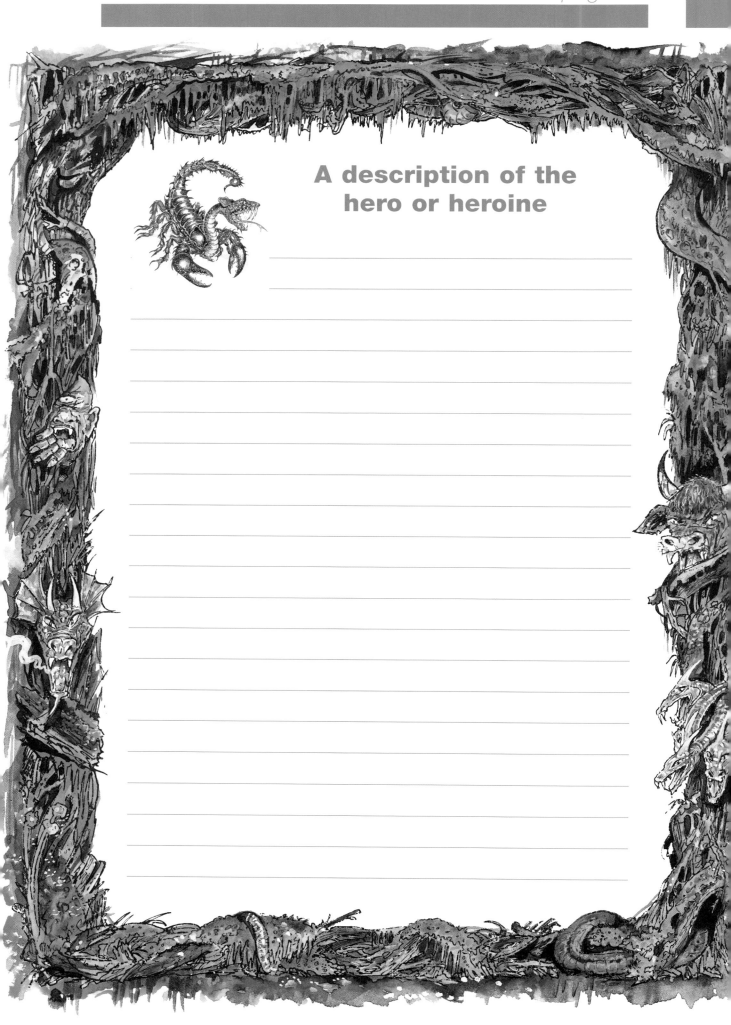

A description of the hero or heroine

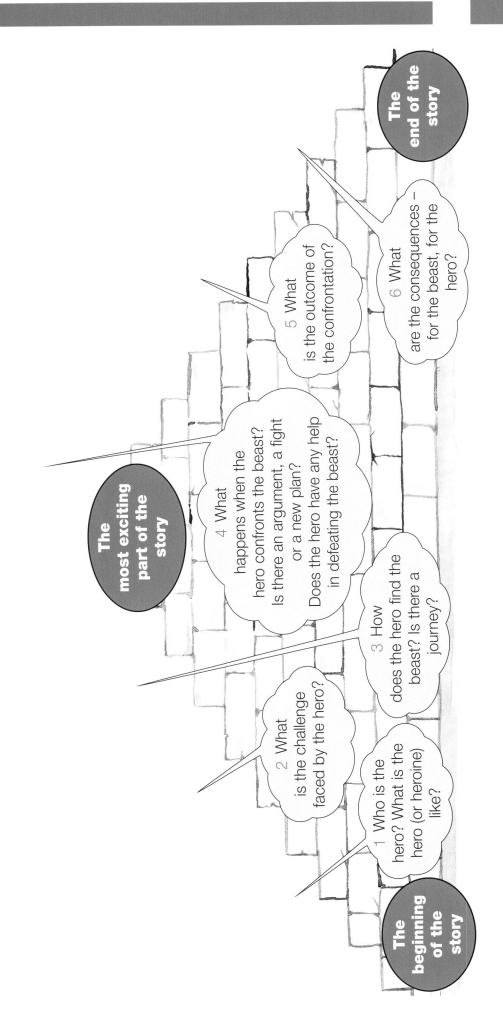

7 He went to King Polydectes and showed him the Gorgon's head. The King was turned to stone. Perseus and his mother were safe at last.

The end of the story

What is the outcome of the confrontation?

What are the consequences – for the beast, for the hero?

6 It was a long and difficult journey. Eventually Perseus got back to Seriphos.

5 Perseus reached the land where the Gorgons lived. He heard their terrible snoring, and the snakes on their heads hissing loudly. He looked in the shield to see their reflection. Then he cut off Medusa's head. The other Gorgons woke up, but Perseus put on the helmet and flew away.

The most exciting part of the story

What happens when the hero confronts the beast? Is there an argument, a fight or a new plan? Does the hero have any help in defeating the beast?

How does the hero find the beast? Is there a journey?

4 Perseus had a long and difficult journey to find the Gorgons. The gods gave him two things to help him: a shiny shield and a sickle to cut off Medusa's head. He tricked the Three Grey Sisters into telling him where to find Medusa. They sent him to the Ocean Nymphs. The Nymphs hated Medusa and agreed to help. They gave him winged sandals so that he could fly to the right place, and a helmet to make him invisible.

3 Medusa was one of three monstrous sisters. They could turn men to stone just by looking at them.

What is the challenge faced by the hero?

2 Perseus was strong and feared nothing. He fought the guards and defended his mother. The king wanted to get rid of Perseus so he sent him on a dangerous mission. Perseus had to go and fetch the head of the Gorgon, Medusa.

Who is the hero? What is the hero (or heroine) like?

1 Long ago, Polydectes was king of Seriphos in Greece. A mother and son called Danae and Perseus lived in the palace. The king wanted to marry Danae but she kept refusing him. Eventually he sent his guards to get her.

The beginning of the story

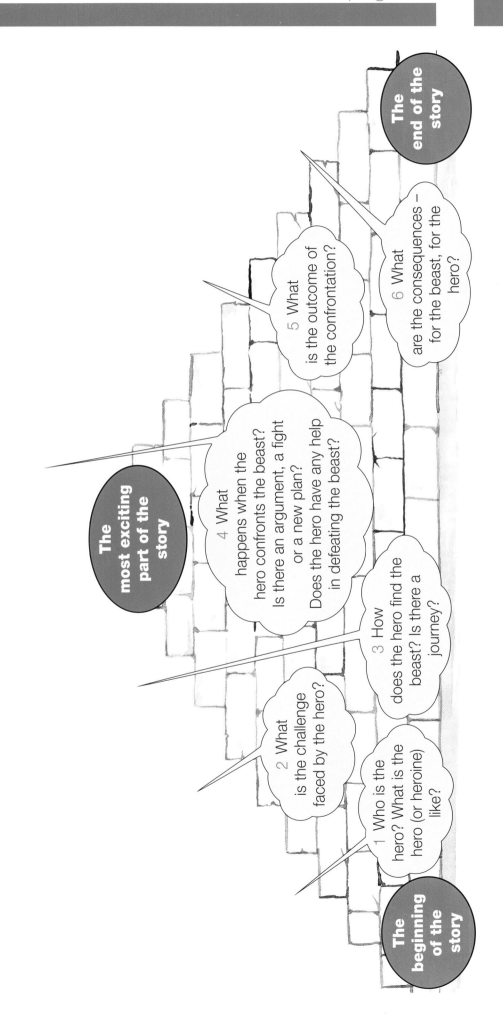

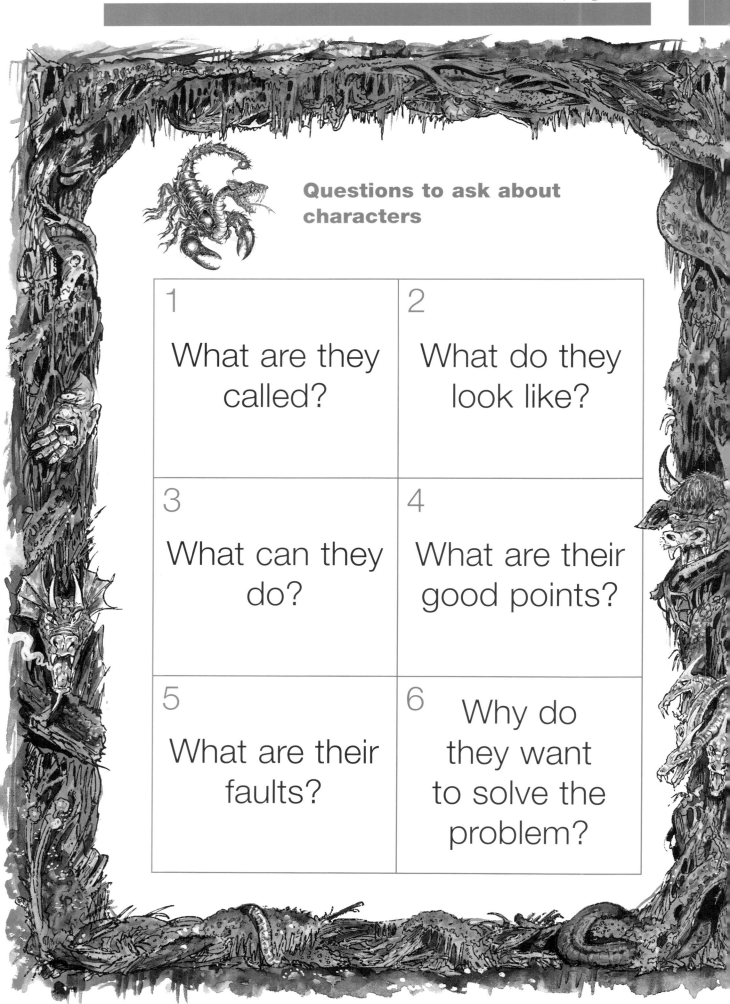

Questions to ask about characters

1 What are they called?	2 What do they look like?
3 What can they do?	4 What are their good points?
5 What are their faults?	6 Why do they want to solve the problem?

(Enlarged copy of paragraph 3 of 'Thespina and the Scorpidon')

When Thespina returned home, her father told her that the Scorpidon had once more been on the rampage, killing and burning everything in its path, as it had done ever since Thespina could remember. Today, it had killed their nearest neighbours. Seven years before, the king had forgotten his promise to the gods that he would share some of his precious treasure with the people. The angry gods decided to punish the king by sending a loathsome monster, known as the Scorpidon, to capture the king's palace and prevent him from seeing his treasure again.

Connectives

Time connectives include:

- when
- whenever
- later
- after a while
- meanwhile
- next
- suddenly
- after that
- moments later
- by this time
- that morning
- days later

(Note: This is not a complete list of all possible time connectives.)

Other connecting words and phrases to join sentences and link ideas include:

- but
- although
- despite
- nevertheless
- however
- until
- as
- in case
- unless
- therefore

(Note: This is not a complete list of all possible connectives.)

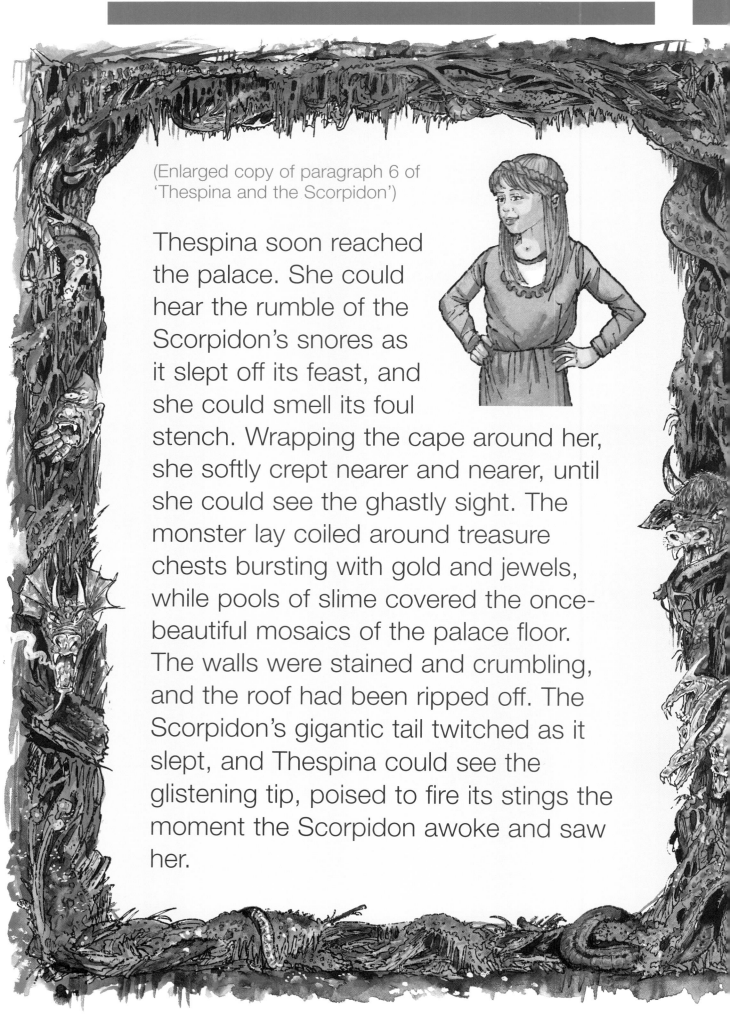

(Enlarged copy of paragraph 6 of 'Thespina and the Scorpidon')

Thespina soon reached the palace. She could hear the rumble of the Scorpidon's snores as it slept off its feast, and she could smell its foul stench. Wrapping the cape around her, she softly crept nearer and nearer, until she could see the ghastly sight. The monster lay coiled around treasure chests bursting with gold and jewels, while pools of slime covered the once-beautiful mosaics of the palace floor. The walls were stained and crumbling, and the roof had been ripped off. The Scorpidon's gigantic tail twitched as it slept, and Thespina could see the glistening tip, poised to fire its stings the moment the Scorpidon awoke and saw her.

Read through your work carefully.
Ask yourself these questions …

Plot

Does the plot make sense?

Is it exciting?

Does anything need explaining more carefully?

Paragraphs

Have I used paragraphs to structure my story?

Have I used connecting words and phrases
to show how paragraphs link?

Description

Have I chosen words and phrases carefully to
help my reader imagine what I am describing?

Sentences

Have I punctuated all my sentences correctly?

Have I used a mixture of short and long
sentences?

Have I used connecting words and phrases
to link sentences together?

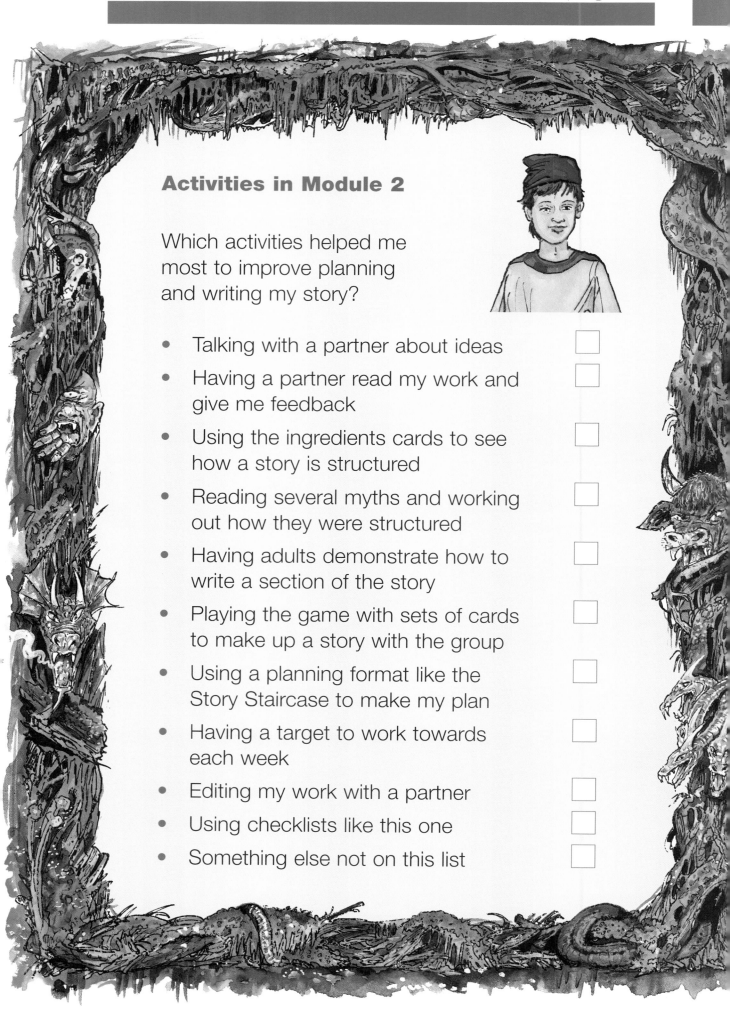

Activities in Module 2

Which activities helped me
most to improve planning
and writing my story?

- Talking with a partner about ideas ☐

- Having a partner read my work and give me feedback ☐

- Using the ingredients cards to see how a story is structured ☐

- Reading several myths and working out how they were structured ☐

- Having adults demonstrate how to write a section of the story ☐

- Playing the game with sets of cards to make up a story with the group ☐

- Using a planning format like the Story Staircase to make my plan ☐

- Having a target to work towards each week ☐

- Editing my work with a partner ☐

- Using checklists like this one ☐

- Something else not on this list ☐

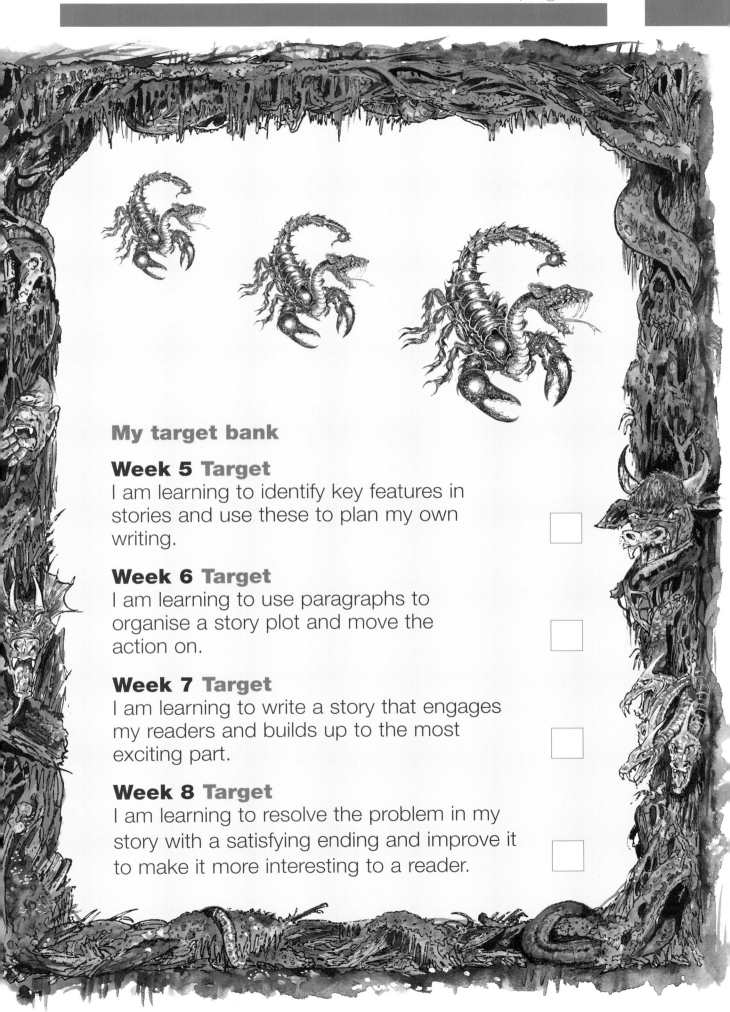

My target bank

Week 5 Target

I am learning to identify key features in stories and use these to plan my own writing.

Week 6 Target

I am learning to use paragraphs to organise a story plot and move the action on.

Week 7 Target

I am learning to write a story that engages my readers and builds up to the most exciting part.

Week 8 Target

I am learning to resolve the problem in my story with a satisfying ending and improve it to make it more interesting to a reader.

Target plan

Week 9	Week 10	Week 11	Week 12
Planning a report	Writing a report	Using and adapting writing for different purposes	Evaluating work and progress

I am learning to identify features of non-chronological reports and use these to plan my writing.	**I am learning to organise and write a report that will give my readers the information they need clearly and simply.**	**I am learning to use and adapt written language for different purposes.**	**I am learning to re-draft, edit and evaluate my work, and reflect on my progress.**

When I am writing to inform I can:
- identify different text types;
- think about the purpose of my writing and decide which text type to use;
- make notes to use for my own writing;
- select important information and reject irrelevant information;
- choose the correct tense and person in which to write;
- organise my ideas into a logical order depending on the text type, e.g. sequence of steps in instructions, or any order after the introduction in a non-chronological report;
- make my writing clear and interesting for the reader by using a mixture of simple and complex sentences;
- adapt my writing for a different purpose, e.g. to amuse an identified audience, by altering words and phrases.

E-mail

From: Zarnon Feevo, Editor-in-Chief, *Encylopaedia Intergalactica*

To: Editorial staff

It is time for a new edition of the *Encylopaedia Intergalactica*. In the present edition, some of the reports about Planet Earth are very inaccurate. For example, see at the bottom of this e-mail what our encyclopaedia says about 'Earth dogs'. It is highly embarrassing that the most important encyclopaedia in the Universe should have printed such nonsense. There must be no such mistakes in future.

Zarnon

Earth dogs

Earth dogs are friendly and kind creatures and for that reason most dogs choose to have Earth people (known as humans) to live in their homes with them. Dogs make good owners and they are usually kind and considerate to the humans that the dogs have chosen as their pets.

For example, it is bad for humans to go without exercise, so dogs make a point of taking their pets out for daily walks. In any park, there will be many dogs carefully exercising their humans. In order to make sure that the humans keep up a good pace and do not get lost or left behind, each dog pulls its human along on a lead.

Dogs know that although humans do not have enough intelligence to bark, they are capable of learning a number of simple tricks. Dogs are patient trainers and they delight in teaching their humans to perform simple tasks – for example throwing a small ball or stick. Dogs wish their humans could learn to fetch the ball or stick and bring it back after they have thrown it, but they are realistic enough to know that this is beyond the intelligence of Earth people.

Dogs know that good pet owners treat their humans gently and so they take care to avoid reminding humans of their inferiority to dogs. Indeed many dogs indulge Earth people by pretending to believe that they are actually owned by their humans. It is a good joke.

Key features of effective reports

Effective reports:

- describe the way things are;

- are written in the present tense;

- provide information clearly and simply;

- focus on general, not particular or personal participants;

- are non-chronological;

- are written in the third person.

E-mail

To: **Zarnon Feevo, Editor-in-Chief,** *Encylopaedia Intergalactica*

From: **Editorial Staff**

Here is the completely rewritten report on 'Dogs on Earth'. We hope it meets with your approval.

Yes, this is much better. It just needs some subheadings. I have done the first two. Please add the rest.

Zarnon Feevo

Dogs on Earth

What dogs are

Dogs are animals which are found all over Planet Earth. There are different breeds of dogs: some are quite small but many are quite large and powerful animals. They all have four legs and a tail and they are usually covered with a furry coat, which may be smooth or shaggy.

Habits

Most dogs have a number of habits in common. They can make two different noises – a growl and a bark. They wag their tails when they are pleased or excited. When taken out by Earth people for a walk, dogs like to stop every now and then to sniff at things they pass, for example trees. It is usual for dogs to wear a strap around their necks called a collar and they are often attached to a line or cord when they are taken out. This line is called a lead.

Many dogs are kept as pets by the Earth people, known as humans. These dogs live in the homes of Earth people and are fed and cared for by the humans. Dogs seem to enjoy being kept as pets and they are usually friendly towards humans and enjoy being near them.

Dogs need to be looked after carefully if they are to stay fit and healthy. They need plenty of exercise and to be properly fed. Earth people buy special dog food which is sold in tins or packets. When dogs become ill, humans take them to a special doctor called a vet.

Some dogs are trained to do special jobs – for example to help humans in their work. Human jobs which sometimes use specially trained dogs include the police and farming. Some dogs are trained to live with human beings in order to help them with tasks that they would otherwise find difficult – for example guide dogs help people who are blind. Some dogs – usually a kind called greyhounds, which are very fast runners – are trained to run in races with other dogs.

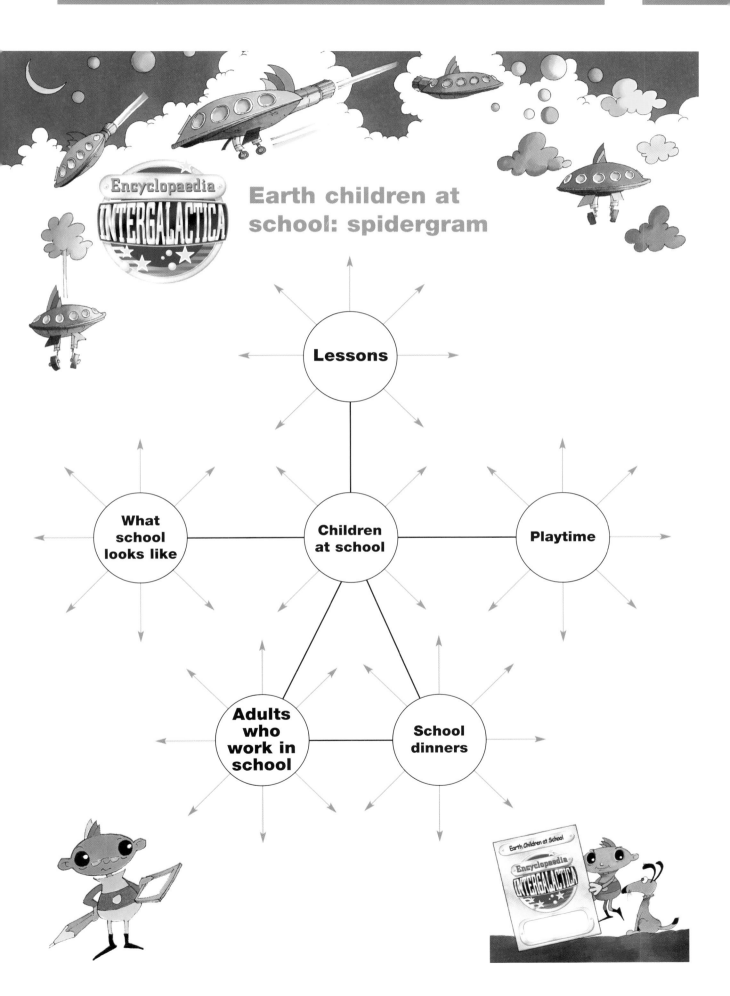

Earth children at school: spidergram

Lessons

What school looks like

Children at school

Playtime

Adults who work in school

School dinners

Dr Xargle's Book of Earthlets
Translated into human by Jeanne Willis

Pictures by Tony Ross

Good morning, class.

Today we are going to learn about Earthlets.

They come in four colours. Pink, brown, black or yellow … but not green.

They have one head and only two eyes, two short tentacles with pheelers on the end and two long tentacles called leggies.

They have square claws which they use to frighten off wild beasts known as Tibbles and Marmaduke.

Earthlets grow fur on their heads but not enough to keep them warm.

They must be wrapped in the hairdo of a sheep.

Very old Earthlings (or 'Grannies') unravel the sheep and with two pointed sticks they make Earthlet wrappers in blue and white and pink.

Earthlets have no fangs at birth.

For many days they drink only milk through a hole in their face.

When they have finished the milk they must be patted and squeezed to stop them exploding.

When they grow a fang, the parent Earthling takes the egg of a hen and mangles it with a prong.

Then she puts the eggmangle on a small spade and tips it into the Earthlet's mouth, nose and ears.

To stop them leaking, Earthlets must be pulled up by the back tentacles and folded in half.

Then they must be wrapped quickly in a fluffy triangle or sealed with paper and glue.

During the day, Earthlets collect the hairs of Tibbles and Marmaduke, mud, eggmangle and banana.

They are then placed in plastic capsules with warm water and a yellow floating bird.

After soaking, Earthlets must be dried carefully to stop them shrinking.

Then they are sprinkled with dust to stop them sticking to things.

Earthlets can be recognised by their fierce cry, 'WAAAAAAA!'

To stop them doing this, the Earthling Daddy picks them up and flings them into the atmosphere.

Then he tries to catch them.

If they still cry, the Earthling Mummy pulls their pheelers one by one and says 'This little piggy went to market' until the Earthlet makes a 'hee hee' noise.

If they still cry, they are sent to a place called beddybyes.

This is a swinging box with a soft lining in which there lives a small bear called Teddy.

That is the end of today's lesson.

If you are all very good and quiet we are going to put our disguises on and visit planet Earth to see some real Earthlets.

The spaceship leaves in five minutes.

From *Dr Xargle's Book of Earthlets* Translated into human by Jeanne Willis (ISBN 1842700677). Used by kind permission of Andersen Press.

Guide for aliens

This report has been carefuly desined to inform aliens clearly and briefly about Earth children at school. This is to prepare them for a possible visit to an Earth school.

The report shows the feetures of a typical school. This is about the people who work in schools, what the children do their, what the playground is like, and so on.

● The instructions show them how to find the nearest Earth school to their landing site.

● Aliens will find this guide very useful when they visit.

Checklist for re-drafting and editing

1 Does it meet the needs of your reader?

- Decide who your reader is.
- Will this text appeal to your reader?
- Will it give them what they need?

2 Have you used complex sentences where they are needed?

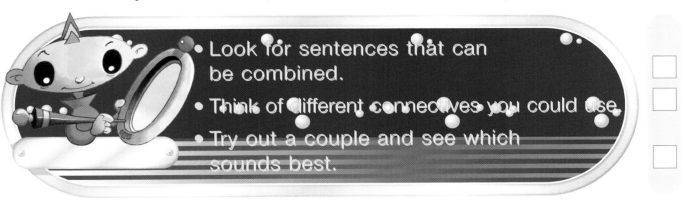

- Look for sentences that can be combined.
- Think of different connectives you could use.
- Try out a couple and see which sounds best.

3 Are any words wrongly spelt?

- Underline the words you think are wrong.
- Think of strategies you could use to help you spell them correctly (e.g. counting syllables, using a mnemonic, sounding it out, etc.).
- If in doubt, check in a dictionary.

Argument planning framework

Use this framework to organise the ideas for your letter.

There are some useful connectives at the bottom of each box that will help you when drafting your argument.

Opening paragraph
Why you are writing and what you want to happen...

Although not everyone would agree…
I believe that…

Main reason to support your argument
... add evidence to back up your point of view...

Firstly…
The most important point is…

Further reason to support your argument
... add evidence to back up your point of view...

Furthermore…
In addition…

Concluding paragraph
Summarise the main points...
Restate your point of view and what you want to happen...

In conclusion…
Therefore…

Things that help me as a learner

- Working with a partner on tasks ☐
- Having planning grids and formats to use ☐
- Having checklists to use while I'm writing ☐
- Making notes using key words ☐
- Making notes using diagrams ☐
- Having a clear target to work to ☐
- Using a checklist to evaluate my work ☐
- Working on my own ☐
- Discussing ideas with a partner ☐
- Presenting work in a different format, e.g. changing written information into a diagram ☐

Add your own ideas if you wish ...

- _____
- _____

My target bank

Week 9 Target

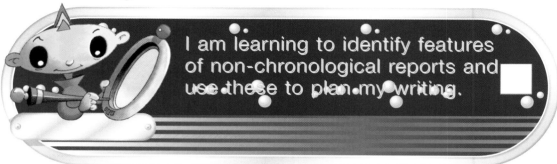

I am learning to identify features of non-chronological reports and use these to plan my writing.

Week 10 Target

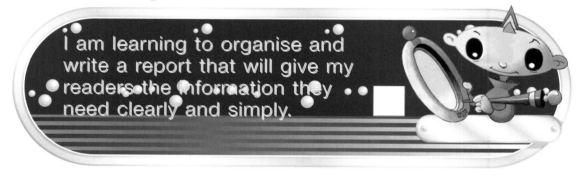

I am learning to organise and write a report that will give my readers the information they need clearly and simply.

Week 11 Target

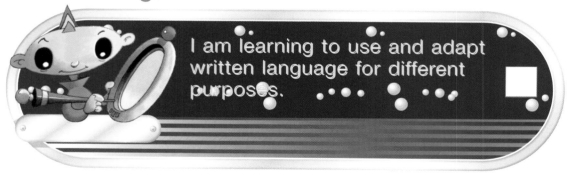

I am learning to use and adapt written language for different purposes.

Week 12 Target

I am learning to re-draft, edit and evaluate my work, and reflect on my progress.

Earth Children at School

Encyclopaedia

INTERGALACTICA

Lessons

Adults who work in school

Adults who work in school (continued)

THE HEADTEACHER
The headteacher is

Playtime

Joke report on playtime

Joke report

Page for re-drafting

WE CAN PERSUADE YOU

Planning grid for instructions for finding the Earth School nearest your landing site

Step 1

Step 2

Step 3

Step 4

Step 5